The Deer and the Earwig
A Poem and a Story

I Hear with my Little Ear

I hear with my little ear. . .

Hooray! Hooray!
A very loud cheer.

I hear with my little ear. . .

A very loud **bump**!
(My dad can't steer.)

I hear with my little ear. . .

A snap of twigs.

It's a very shy deer.

The Deer and the Earwig

Here is a stream. Here is a deer.

And here is a little black earwig.

Oh dear! The earwig has fallen into the stream!
"Help! Help!" he cries.

"Do not fear, I am here," says the deer.
She drops a leaf into the stream.

The earwig climbs on to the leaf.
He sails to the bank.

"Thank you, deer," says the earwig.
"You saved my life."

A week later. . .
Here is the stream. Here is the deer.
And here is the little black earwig.

Oh dear! Here is a hunter!
He has a spear.

The deer can't see the hunter.
She can't hear him.

Help! The hunter lifts his spear.

But here comes the earwig.

"Do not fear, I am here!" he says.

The earwig nips the hunter's ear.
The hunter jumps and drops the spear.

The deer runs away.

"Thank you, earwig," says the deer.
"You saved my life."